Flute Exam Pieces

ABRSM Grade 1

Selected from the 2018–2021 syllabus

Name _Lc_

C000051068

Date of exam

Contents

page

Consultant Editor for ABRSM: David Blackwell
Footnotes: Anthony Burton and Richard Jones (RJ)

Other pieces for Grade 1

First published in 2017 by ABRSM (Publishing) Ltd,
a wholly owned subsidiary of ABRSM, 4 London Wall Place,
London EC2Y 5AU, United Kingdom
© 2017 by The Associated Board of the Royal Schools of Music
Distributed worldwide by Oxford University Press

Music origination by Julia Bovee
Cover by Kate Benjamin & Andy Potts
Printed in England by Caligraving Ltd, Thetford, Norfolk
on materials from sustainable sources.

A:1

Bourrée

from *Sechs musicalische Partien*

Arranged and edited
by Richard Jones

Johann Krieger
(1651–1735)

Here is a good example of a bourrée: a fairly quick and lively French dance, though in this case written by a German composer. The dance type is in duple time, so would be felt as two minim beats per bar, despite the time signature. This Bourrée was originally a keyboard piece – it belonged to a collection of dances by Johann Krieger for spinet or clavichord. (RJ) **The first repeat should be observed in the exam**, but the ornaments are optional.

Source: *Sechs musicalische Partien* (Nuremberg: W. M. Endter, 1697). In this arrangement, the original keyboard right-hand part is played on the flute, the keyboard left hand remains unchanged, and the new keyboard right hand is editorial. All dynamics, slurs, staccatos and ornaments are editorial suggestions only.

© 2017 by The Associated Board of the Royal Schools of Music

Cradle Song

Op. 49 No. 4

Arranged by Ian Denley

Johannes Brahms
(1833–97)

Brahms composed his famous 'Lullaby', originally called *Wiegenlied* or 'Cradle Song', in 1848 for his Viennese friends Arthur and Bertha Faber, to celebrate the birth of their son Hans. The gently rocking accompaniment is based on a popular Viennese love song which Bertha had sung to Brahms ten years earlier, when she was a 17-year-old member of a Ladies' Choir which he conducted. Brahms wrote to the couple that he imagined Bertha singing Hans to sleep while Arthur murmured a love song to her.

© 1998 by The Associated Board of the Royal Schools of Music
Adapted from *Time Pieces for Flute*, Volume 1, selected and arranged by Ian Denley (ABRSM)

The woman is fickle

La donna è mobile

from *Rigoletto*

A:3

Arranged by Nancy Litten

Giuseppe Verdi
(1813–1901)

Verdi's 1851 opera *Rigoletto* is set in the 16th century in the north Italian city of Mantua. The plot centres on the arrogant, immoral Duke of Mantua, his court jester Rigoletto and Rigoletto's daughter Gilda. The aria 'La donna è mobile' is sung in Act III by the Duke in a tavern. The staccato markings in the melodic line help give the piece its swagger.

Lazy Sunday

from *Playaround* for Flute, Book 3

B:1

Roma Cafolla
(born 1949)

Roma Cafolla is a Northern Irish composer. Amongst the large amount of educational music she has written are the graded *Playaround* volumes. The swung quavers give this piece a mood of weekend relaxation, but also notice the metronome marking: the piece may not be as lazy as you think!

The Easy Winners

Arranged by David Blackwell

Scott Joplin
(1867/8–1917)

Scott Joplin grew up in Texas, the son of a former slave, and became, as he called himself, 'the King of Ragtime Writers' – a pioneer in print of the ragtime style, which combines the regular tread of marches and dances with the syncopations of African American tradition. This is the first strain of a 'ragtime two-step', which he published in St Louis in 1901. The tempo marking 'Not fast' is an instruction which Joplin repeated in many publications. Note, too, that the classic ragtime style is not thought to have involved swung rhythms: even quavers give the piece its characteristic strutting movement.

The Pelican from Heligan

No. 1 from *Creature Comforts*, Grades 1–3

Mark Tanner
(born 1963)

B:3

Mark Tanner is a well-known British pianist in concert halls and on cruise liners; he has also taught at school and college level, written reviews and articles for many magazines, as well as a book called *The Mindful Pianist*, and composed more than sixty albums of educational music. This is the first item in a graded collection of 'animal-inspired pieces': The Lost Gardens of Heligan are a popular visitor attraction in Cornwall, England, but the pelican is a rare bird in the county, so the title must have been chosen for its pleasing sound! The composer says that the piece is 'both quirky and fun to play; its recurring jaunty rhythms encourage quite a laid-back approach, but are best suited to a firmly rooted tempo.'

C:1

Click Here

No. 2 from *Jazz@Etudes* for Flute

Mark Nightingale
(born 1967)

Mark Nightingale is a well-known jazz trombonist, the leader of several groups including a Big Band, whose repertoire features his own compositions and arrangements, and also much in demand as a member of other bands. He has written many studies and concert pieces for various instruments. In this study, with its computer-inspired title, the rests are as important as the notes.

Study in F

from *Erster Flöten-Unterricht*, Op. 387

Wilhelm Popp
(1828–1903)

Wilhelm Popp was a flautist of the court orchestra in his native Coburg, in central Germany, and later principal flautist of the Hamburg Philharmonic Orchestra. He published a vast amount of music for his own instrument – as you can see by the opus number of his *Erster Flöten-Unterricht* (*Flute Method for Beginners*), from which this study is taken. The character of the piece is established by its staccato markings and detailed phrasing.

Source: *Erster Flöten-Unterricht*, Op. 387 (Leipzig: Peters 1887). The dynamics are editorial suggestions only. The staccato dots on the final crotchets of bars 7 and 13 are editorial.

Snow Walk

No. 1 from *42 More Modern Studies for Solo Flute*

James Rae
(born 1957)

The British musician James Rae is a performer on clarinet and saxophone, a teacher, and the composer of over 120 volumes of music for student wind players. This is the opening piece in a second volume of studies in a variety of musical styles 'designed to improve the student's musical as well as technical abilities.' The piece is in G Dorian mode. The moderate tempo helps to suggest the feeling of trudging through snow.

© Copyright 2014 by Universal Edition A. G. Wien/UE 21647
Reproduced by permission. All rights reserved.